The Folksinger's Guide To
The Classical Guitar

HARVEY VINSON

Oak Publications, New York
Music Sales Limited, London

The Folksinger's Guide To
The Classical Guitar

Dedicated to Diane

Book design by Jean Hammons

Copyright © 1971 by Oak Publications,
A Division of Embassy Music Corporation, New York, NY.

International Standard Book Number: 0.8256.0065.0
Library of Congress Catalog Card Number: 74-136358

Exclusive Distributors:
Music Sales Corporation
225 Park Avenue South, New York, NY 10003 USA
Music Sales Limited
8/9 Frith Street, London W1V 5TZ England
Music Sales Pty. Limited
120 Rothschild Street, Rosebery, Sydney, NSW 2018, Australia

Printed in the United States of America by
Island Book Factory

CONTENTS

continued

FOREWORD

This book was compiled to meet the demands of the growing number of folk and rock guitarists who are anxious to play compositions written for the classic guitar. It does presuppose some familiarity with the instrument and some ability to play. It is not an instruction book. In the hands of a competant classic guitar teacher it makes an excellent supplement to his teaching.

A complete tablature instruction is presented in the first few pages to help you understand this type of music notation. Below each staff of tablature is the music in regular notes. This will aid in learning to read music notes.

Within these pages are some of the most beautiful compositions ever written for the guitar. Your technique and hearing cannot help but improve with the mastering of some of these pieces.

READING TABLATURE

Playing from tablature is an old and honorable tradition. Even as far back as the 15th century, organ music was commonly notated in tablature. In the 16th century, almost all lute music was scored in tablature. The immense popularity of tablature in the past can be accorded to one primary reason: that reading music from tablature is very easy.

The guitar* has six strings, and the tablature system used in this book (based on a combination of the Spanish and French tablature systems) uses six lines:

The guitar string that is the lowest in pitch is indicated by the bottom line.

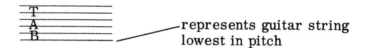

The guitar string that is the next lowest in pitch is indicated by the second line from the bottom.

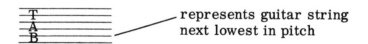

Continuing in the same manner, the string highest in pitch is indicated by the top line.

*Most of the compositions in this book were written for the so called "classic" guitar. The characteristics of this type of guitar are a round sound-hole and nylon strings. However, they may be effectively played on a steel string guitar, electric or otherwise.

Most modern guitars have at least 18 frets. These frets are numbered from *1* to *18* beginning with the fret nearest the tuning gear.

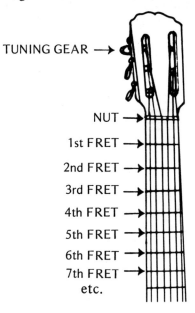

TUNING GEAR →

NUT →
1st FRET →
2nd FRET →
3rd FRET →
4th FRET →
5th FRET →
6th FRET →
7th FRET →
etc.

If you were to see the number "1" on the top line of the tablature, you would play the 1st string (the highest in pitch) while fretting it at the 1st fret.

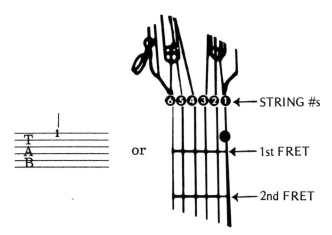

or

STRING #s

1st FRET

2nd FRET

If the "1" appeared on the second line from the top of the tablature, you would play the 2nd string (the string 2nd highest in pitch) while fretting it at the 1st fret.

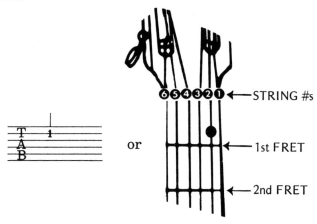

or

STRING #s

1st FRET

2nd FRET

An "o" on a tablature line indicates that you play the string "open" or unfingered by the left hand. And "o" on the top line of the tablature indicates that you play the string highest in pitch with the left hand not touching it.

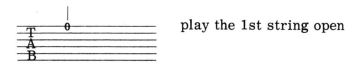

play the 1st string open

In order to indicate which *right hand* finger is used to pluck a string, the abbreviations *i, m, r,* and *t* are used.

i = index finger
m = middle finger
r = ring finger
t = thumb

To make sure you understand what we've covered so far, play the following example. Count slowly and evenly from *1* to *4* over and over playing one note on each count (or beat).

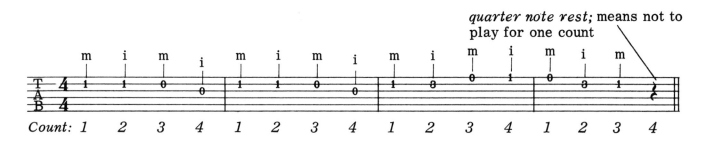

quarter note rest; means not to play for one count

Count: 1   2   3   4   1   2   3   4   1   2   3   4   1   2   3   4

One last feature of the tablature system concerning the right hand is the note stem.

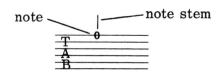

note   note stem

10

The note stem either points up, as in the last few examples or it points down.

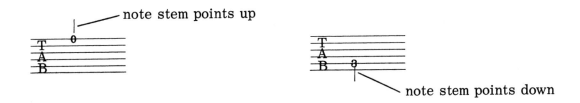

note stem points up

note stem points down

When the stem points up, you play the note with a right hand *finger*. When the stem points down, play it with the right hand *thumb*. When a note has two stems pointing both ways, play that note with the thumb.

play both  and with the right hand thumb.

Try the next example to make sure you understand this.

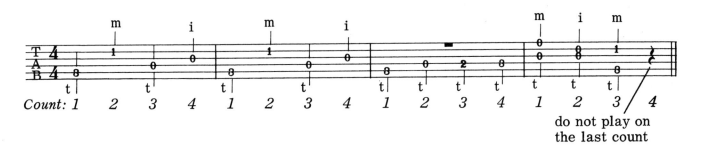

Count: 1 2 3 4 1 2 3 4 1 2 3 4 1 2 3 4

do not play on the last count

To indicate the left hand fingering, the numbers *1* through *4* are used.

1 = index finger
2 = middle finger
3 = ring finger
4 = pinky

11

Here is the last music example with the proper left hand fingering. The fingering indications below the tablature are for the notes the thumb plays. Above the tablature are for the notes the fingers play.

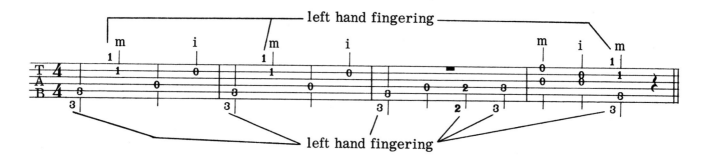

Frequently the left hand fingering and the fret number are the same (examine the last example). When this is so, the left hand fingering is often omitted.

When several strings are plucked simultaneously, the left and right hand fingerings are stacked on top except for the thumb note. Examine and play the following.

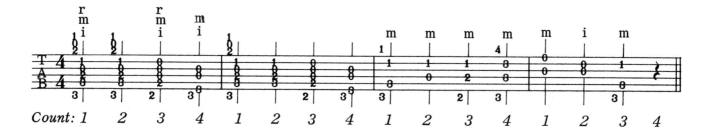

Now for some theory. The vertical lines (called bar lines) on the tablature system divide it into measures.

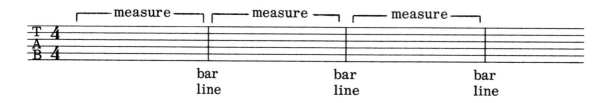

The $\frac{4}{4}$ at the beginning of the tablature system indicates that there are four counts (or beats in each measure. This means that you count from *1* to *4* throughout the entire piece.

The one last thing to learn about before you start the first piece is the tie. The tie looks like this in music notation.

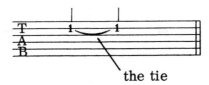

the tie

When two notes are tied together, play the first note and sustain the tone from the first note through the second. In the next example, play on the first count and sustain the sound through the second count without plucking the string again.

do not play here

Below each tablature system is the music notated in actual music notes. If you read music or you are trying to learn, the music notated in regular notes will be of great assistance.

When you are first learning a piece, practice it *slowly* and *evenly* until you can play it without making mistakes. Then gradually speed it up until it reaches the speed indicated at the upper left hand corner of the music. Also, be sure to read all indicated foot-notes.

Study

FERNANDO SOR
(1778–1839)

* ♩ is a quarter note rest. Do not play on the fourth count.

** ≣ is a repeat sign. It means to repeat the piece from the beginning and then go on. There should be no rhythmic hesitancy when going from this measure back to the first measure.

*** ≣ is also a repeat sign. With repeat signs you either return to the beginning of the piece or the facing repeat sign: ≣ In this case repeat back to the beginning of the ninth measure.

EIGHT NOTES—QUARTER AND HALF NOTE RESTS

Up to this point you have only been concerned with notes with a single stem.

These notes are called *quarter notes*. They are so called because four of them can be played in one measure as in this example:

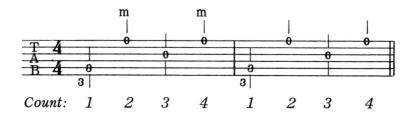

Another important note value is the eighth note which has a single flag on the stem.

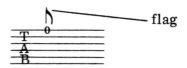

This note is called an eighth note because eight of them can be played in one measure. Insert "&" between the numbers when you count to get the correct rhythmic feel of eighth notes.

You usually find eighth notes barred together. With bars, the last example looks like this:

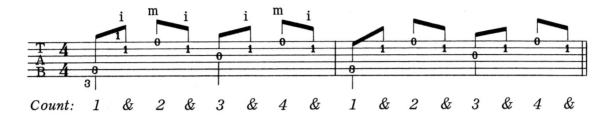

Count: 1 & 2 & 3 & 4 & 1 & 2 & 3 & 4 &

You commonly find four eighth notes barred together as in the next example. This makes eighth notes quite easy to read.

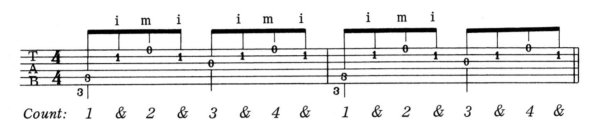

Count: 1 & 2 & 3 & 4 & 1 & 2 & 3 & 4 &

The quarter note rest ⸜ which was introduced in the last piece indicates that you do not play for the time value of a quarter note or one count.

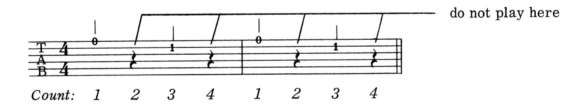

do not play here

Count: 1 2 3 4 1 2 3 4

Occasionally you will find the quarter note rest referring only to the thumb while the fingers continue to play.

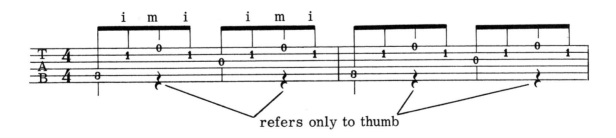

refers only to thumb

Another important rest sign is the half note rest.

half note rest

This rest indicates you do not play for two counts.

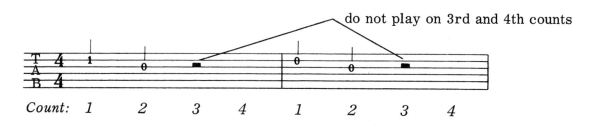

do not play on 3rd and 4th counts

Count: 1   2   3   4   1   2   3   4

As with the quarter note rest, the half note rest occasionally refers only to the thumb while the fingers continue to play (or vice versa). Both rest signs are illustrated in the next piece.

Prelude

MATTEO CARCASSI
(1792-1853)

*The half-note rest and the quarter-note rest combine here to give you a total of three counts of rests in this measure. Play the indicated note on the first count then observe the rests for the remainder of the measure.

REPEAT SIGNS

This next piece uses a combination of quarter notes and eighth notes. Remember that quarter notes are played one on each count and eighth notes are played two on each count.

Also recall that the repeat sign ⫾ indicates that you repeat from

the beginning of the piece or from the facing repeat sign: ⫾⫾

Hungarian Air

BATHIOLI
(19th Century)

*The note the middle finger plays is sustained through the 4th count
while the thumb notes, which are not tied, function normally.

EIGHTH NOTE RESTS

The two following pieces make use of still another rest sign: the eighth note rest.

eighth note rest

The eighth note rest indicates that you do not play for one-half beat. Count and play the following to better understand this.

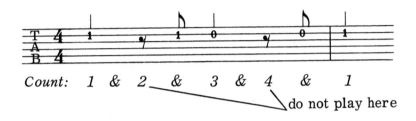

Count: 1   &   2   &   3   &   4   &   1

do not play here

As with the other rest signs, the eighth note rest frequently refers only to the thumb while the fingers continue to play.

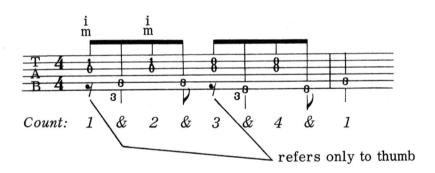

Count: 1   &   2   &   3   &   4   &   1

refers only to thumb

Air in C

FERNANDO SOR

Quickly

Air

MATTEO CARCASSI

*Unlike the other pieces presented thus far, this piece begins on the
3rd count. After you play the 2nd count before the repeat sign, return immediately to the first measure for the 3rd count.

$\frac{2}{4}$ TIME SIGNATURE

The $\frac{4}{4}$ found at the beginning of each piece presented thus far is properly called a *time signature*. With a $\frac{4}{4}$ time signature you play four counts in each measure throughout the entire piece. Another important time signature is $\frac{2}{4}$. With a $\frac{2}{4}$ time signature, you play *two* counts in each measure throughout the entire piece. Count, "1 . . . 2 . . . 1 . . .2 . . .," slowly and evenly and play the following example.

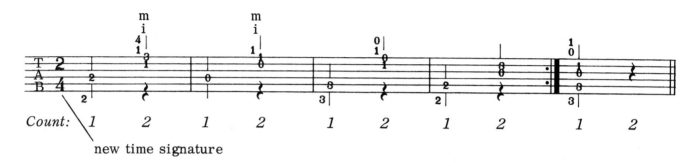

With eighth notes insert "&" between each count.

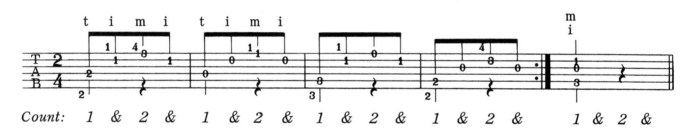

Study

ANTON DIABELLI
(1781–1853)

SIXTEENTH NOTES

For the next piece you have to learn a new note value: the sixteenth note. The sixteenth note has *two* flags on its stem.

Sixteenth notes are often played in groups of four. When this is so, they are generally barred together.

Four sixteenth notes have the same time value as two eighth notes or one quarter note. This means that you can play four sixteenth notes on one count (or beat). Count, *"1-a-&-a . . . 2-a-&-a,"* in order to subdivide each count into four equal parts. Count and play the following example slowly and evenly.

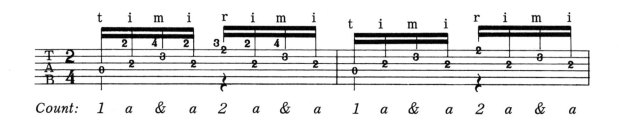

Count: 1 a & a 2 a & a   1 a & a 2 a & a

Prelude

Moderately

MATTEO CARCASSI

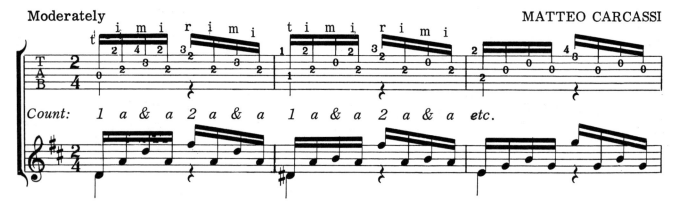

Count: 1 a & a 2 a & a   1 a & a 2 a & a *etc.*

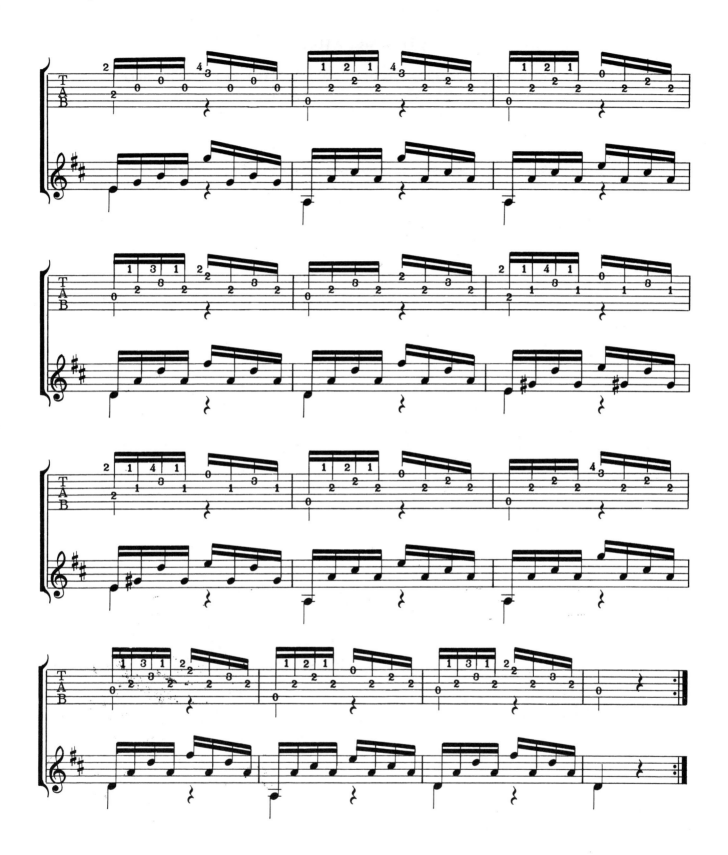

$\frac{3}{4}$ TIME SIGNATURE

Another important time signature to learn is $\frac{3}{4}$. The top half of the time signature indicates the number of counts in each measure: with $\frac{4}{4}$ there are four counts in each measure, with $\frac{2}{4}$ there are two counts in each measure, and with $\frac{3}{4}$ there are three counts in each measure.

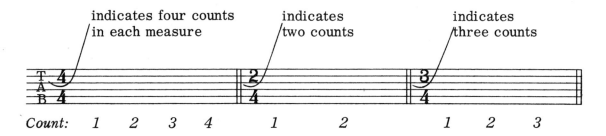

Count slowly and evenly from *1* to *3* and play the following example:

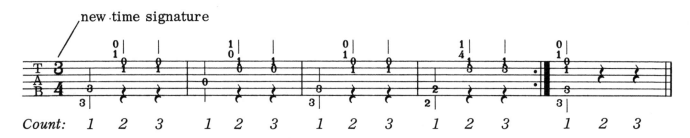

28

Study

FERNANDO CARULLI
(1770-1841)

Fine

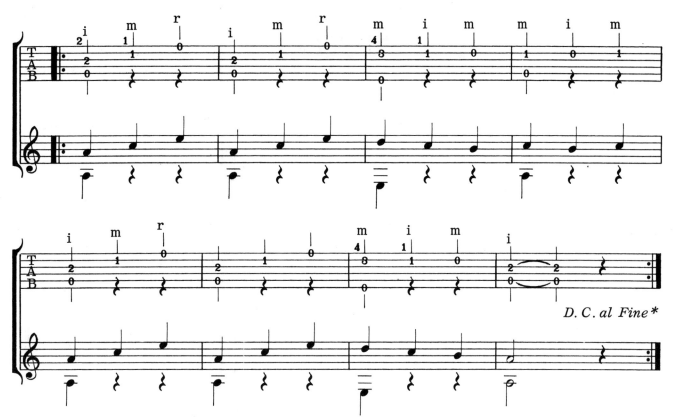

D. C. is an abbreviation of *da capo* (It. *capo*, head) meaning "from the beginning." The term indicates that you repeat the piece from the beginning and end it at a certain place marked *fine* (*da capo al fine*). Be sure to repeat the last eight measures before you return to the beginning.

With eighth notes insert "&" between each count.

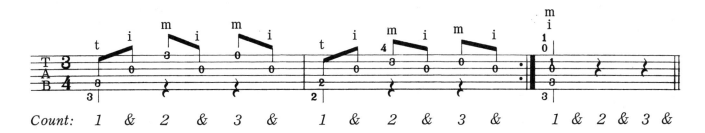

Count: 1   &   2   &   3   &   1   &   2   &   3   &   1 & 2 & 3 &

Study

MAURO GIULIANI
(1780-1840)

Moderately

Count: 1 & 2 & 3 & 1 & 2 & 3 & etc.

Prelude

MATTEO CARCASSI

$\frac{3}{8}$ TIME SIGNATURE

A new type of time signature that we'll take up now is the $\frac{3}{8}$ time signature. Like the $\frac{3}{4}$ time signature, the $\frac{3}{8}$ time signature has three counts in each measure.

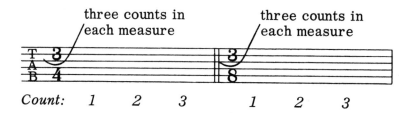

The basic difference between these two signatures is that with the $\frac{3}{4}$ time signature you play one quarter note (or its equivalent) on each count; with the $\frac{3}{8}$ time signature you play one *eighth* note (or its equivalent) on each count. The bottom half of the time signature indicates the value of the note played on each count.

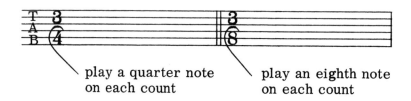

Play the following short example to make sure you understand this new time signature.

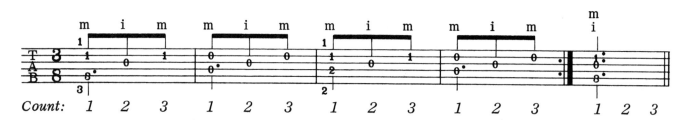

A note frequently used in the $\frac{3}{8}$ time signature is the dotted quarter note.

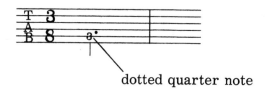

dotted quarter note

Placing a dot after a note increases its time value by one-half. A dotted quarter note is equivalent to a quarter note plus an eighth note (an eighth note has one-half the time value of a quarter note).

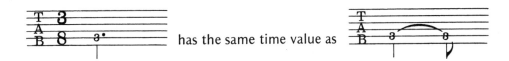

has the same time value as

The dotted quarter note is held for three counts or an entire measure when used with a $\frac{3}{8}$ time signature.

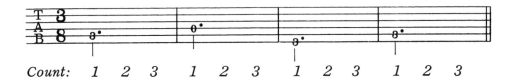

Count: *1   2   3   1   2   3   1   2   3   1   2   3*

Waltz

L. MEIGNEN
(19th Century)

Quarter notes and sixteenth notes are also used with the $\frac{3}{8}$ time signature. Quarter notes receive two counts with this signature.

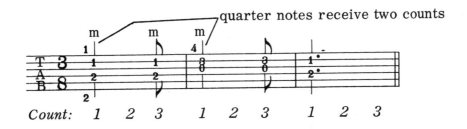

Play two sixteenth notes for each count with this signature. Insert "&" between each number when you count.

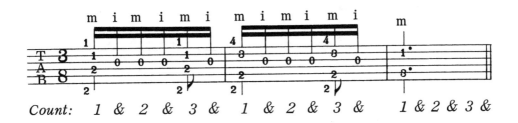

Study

MAURO GIULIANI

38

*When two notes of different pitches are tied together, the effect is called a *slur*. The slur is achieved in this case by playing the 3rd string open with the index finger of the right hand and, while the note is still sounding, "hammering on" the 2nd finger of the left hand behind the 2nd fret. This causes the 3rd string to sound at the 2nd fret without the use of the right hand.

THE TIE

Play the following example carefully noting the tie in the second measure.

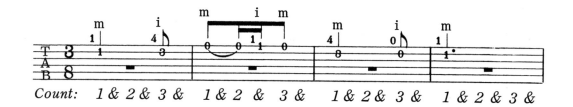

Count: 1 & 2 & 3 &   1 & 2 & 3 &   1 & 2 & 3 &   1 & 2 & 3 &

Recall that placing a dot after a note increases that note's value by one half. A dotted eighth note is equivalent to an eighth note plus a sixteenth note (a sixteenth note has one-half the time value of an eighth note).

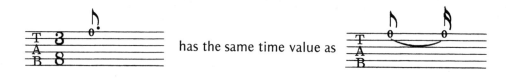

Therefore

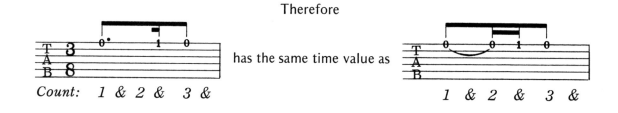

The first example could be notated as follows. Play it and compare.

Count: 1 & 2 & 3 &   1 & 2 & 3 &   1 & 2 & 3 &   1 & 2 & 3 &

Greensleeves

Anonymous
(16th Century)

Count:* 3 &   1&2&3 &   1 & 2 & 3 &   etc.

*This piece begins on the 3rd beat.

Count: 1&2&3 & 1&2&3 & etc.

⁶₈ TIME SIGNATURE

A new time signature to consider is the ⁶₈ time signature. Unlike any time signature we've taken up so far, the ⁶₈ time signature has *six* counts in each measure.

six count in each measure

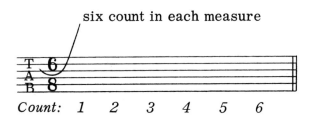

Two measures in the ³₈ time signature have approximately the same rhythmic feeling as one measure in the ⁶₈ time signature.

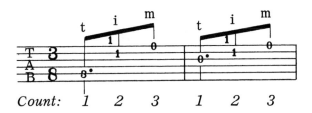

has approximately the same rhythmic feeling as

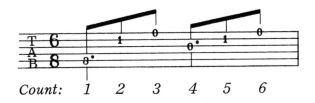

In the following example the 1st and the 4th counts slightly louder than the other counts. This is the correct rhythm using the ⁶₈ time signature.

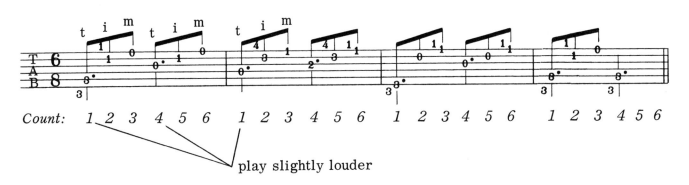

Prelude

FERNANDO CARULLI

Study

FERNANDO CARULLI

Count: 6   1 2 3 4 5 6   1 2 3 4 5 6   etc.

Count: 1 2 3 4 5

6   1 2 3 4 5 6   etc.

*This piece begins on the 6th count.

46

47

Dance

Anonymous
(16th Century)

*This piece begins on the 5th count.

Prelude

FERNANDO CARULLI

COLLECTION OF EASY PIECES

The rest of the book contains very little in the way of new technical information. The pieces become gradually more difficult. If you wish, you may choose to work on pieces that are more challenging at first and save the easier ones for later. They all deserve at least one play.

Prelude

DIONISIO AGUADO
(1789–1849)

Villanella

FABRITIO CAROSO
(16th Century)

Study

FERNANDO SOR

Slowly

Count: 6   1 2 3   4 5 6   1 etc.

DOTTED QUARTER NOTE

The dotted quarter note that was used with the $\frac{3}{8}$ and $\frac{6}{8}$ time signatures can also be used with the $\frac{4}{4}$ time signature.

dotted quarter note

Since the time value of a quarter note with the $\frac{4}{4}$ time signature is one count, when the quarter note is dotted*, the time value is one count plus one-half a count.

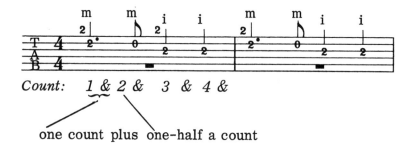

Placing a dot after a note increases its time value by one-half.

Villanicco

CESARE NEGRI
(16th Century)

*This piece begins on the 4th count. Start by counting, "4..&..1..&
..2..3..etc."

Study

MAURO GIULIANI

Quickly

Theme and Variations

FERNANDO CARULLI

Variation I

Count: 1 & 2 & 3 & 1 & 2 & 3 & etc.

59

Variation II

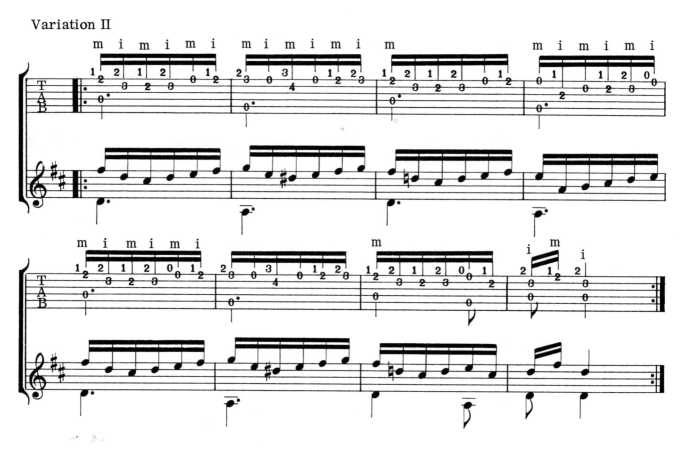

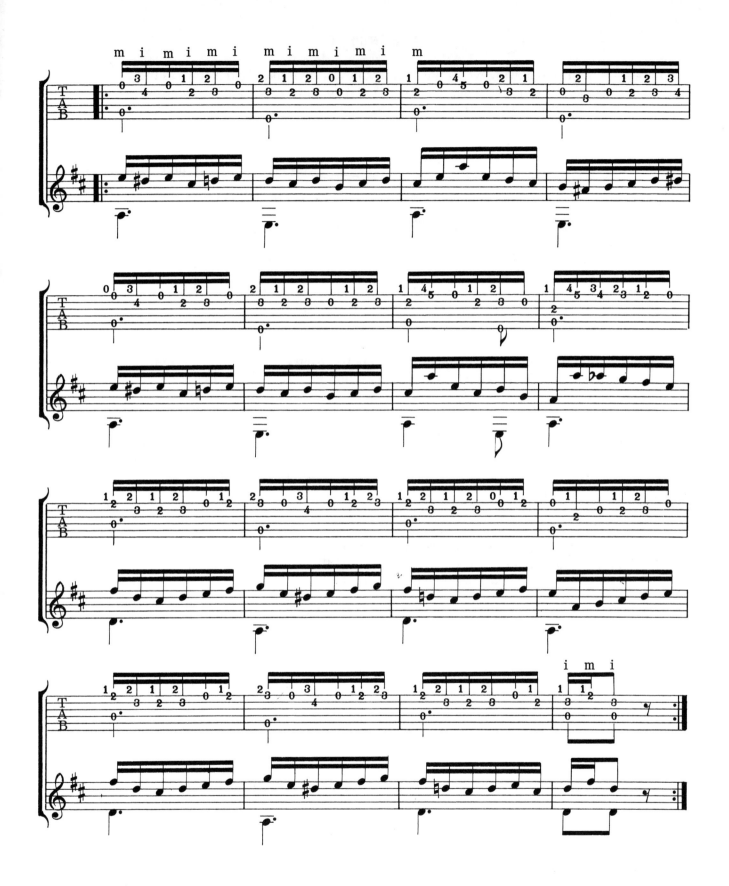

61

THE TRIPLET

The following pieces use a rather unusual rhythmic figure known as the *triplet*. The triplet (indicated by ⌐3¬) is quite easy to play if you will count, "tri-pa-let . . . tri-pa-let," subdividing each count into three equal parts. Note that the example uses a $\frac{2}{4}$ time signature.

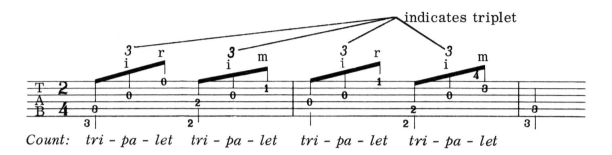

Count: tri – pa – let   tri – pa – let   tri – pa – let   tri – pa – let

Playing triplets and regular eighth notes together is a little tricky. In the next example try keeping a constant rhythm by tapping your foot on each count.

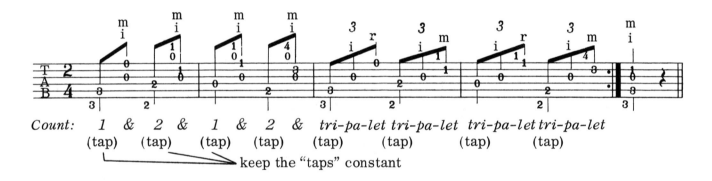

Count: 1 & 2 & 1 & 2 & tri-pa-let tri-pa-let tri-pa-let tri-pa-let
       (tap) (tap) (tap) (tap) (tap) (tap) (tap) (tap)

keep the "taps" constant

The following composition uses quarter notes, eighth notes, triplets, and sixteenth notes. The effect of using progressively smaller note values is to increase the density of sound as well as to raise the tension level as the piece is played. A very steady rhythm is necessary for this compositional technique to be effective.

Study

Moderately

MAURO GIULIANI

Count: 1 2 1 2 etc.

Count: tri-pa-let tri-pa-let etc.

Count: 1 a & a 2 a & a etc.

Waltz

FERNANDO CARULLI

Moderately

Fine

D. C. al Fine

Study

MAURO GIULIANI

Air in E minor

Moderately slow

FERNANDO SOR

Count: *6* *1 2 3 4 5 6* *etc.*

THE FERMATA

The next piece makes use of the fermata sign: 𝄐 When this sign
appears above a note, pause briefly and then continue.

Study

FERNANDO CARULLI

ANOTHER USE OF THE TIE

Play the following example carefully noting the use of the tie.

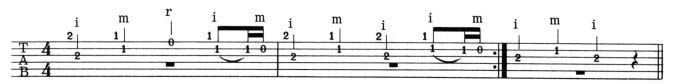

Count: *1 a & a 2 a & a 3 a & a 4 a & a   1 a & a 2 a & a 3 a & a 4 a & a   1a & a 2a & a 3a & a 4*

Since placing a dot after a note increases its time value by one-half, a dotted eighth note is equivalent to an eighth note plus a sixteenth note.

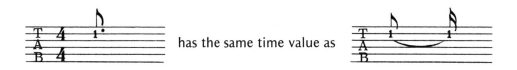

Therefore,

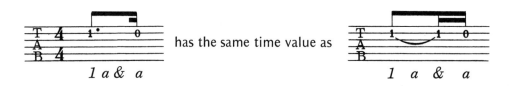

The first example could be notated as follows. Inserting "-a" only after the "&" gives you a better feel for this rhythm.

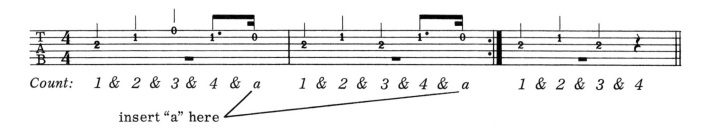

Count: *1 & 2 & 3 & 4 & a   1 & 2 & 3 & 4 & a   1 & 2 & 3 & 4*

insert "a" here

74

Study

DIONISIO AGUADO

Quickly

Count: 4 & a   1 & 2 & 3 & 4 & a   etc.

76

Rondo

FERNANDO CARULLI

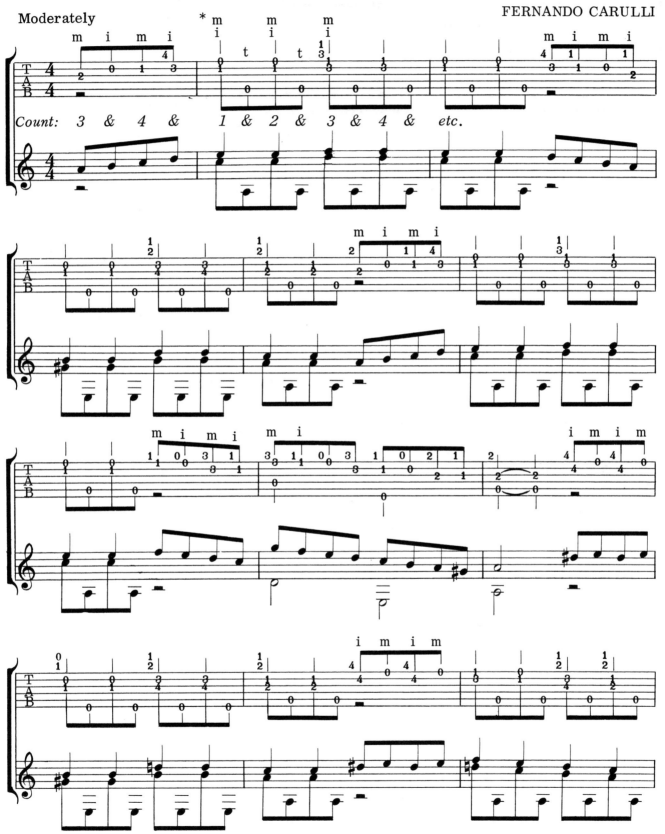

*For ease in note reading, notes to be played by the right hand fingers are occasionally notated with their stems pointing down as in this piece.

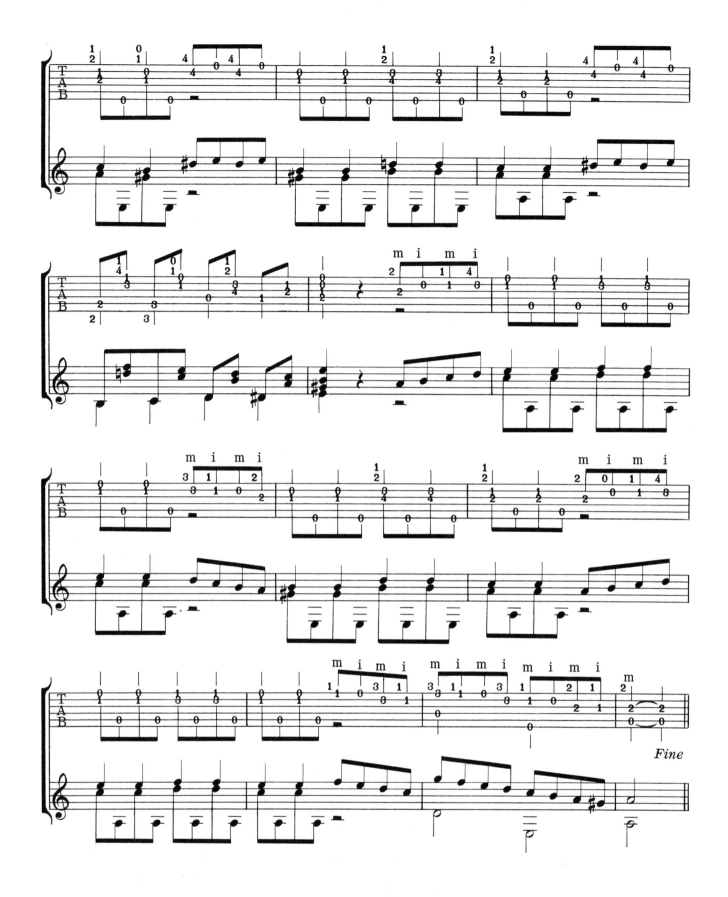

78

D. C. al Fine

SIXTEENTH NOTE REST

A new rest to learn is the sixteenth note rest: ⅞ Like the sixteenth note, this rest also has two flags:

two flags

The sixteenth note rest has the same time value in silence as the sixteenth note has in sound. Play this example.

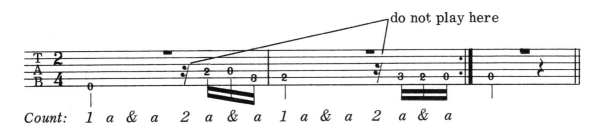

do not play here

Count: 1 a & a 2 a & a 1 a & a 2 a & a

Study

MAURO GIULIANI

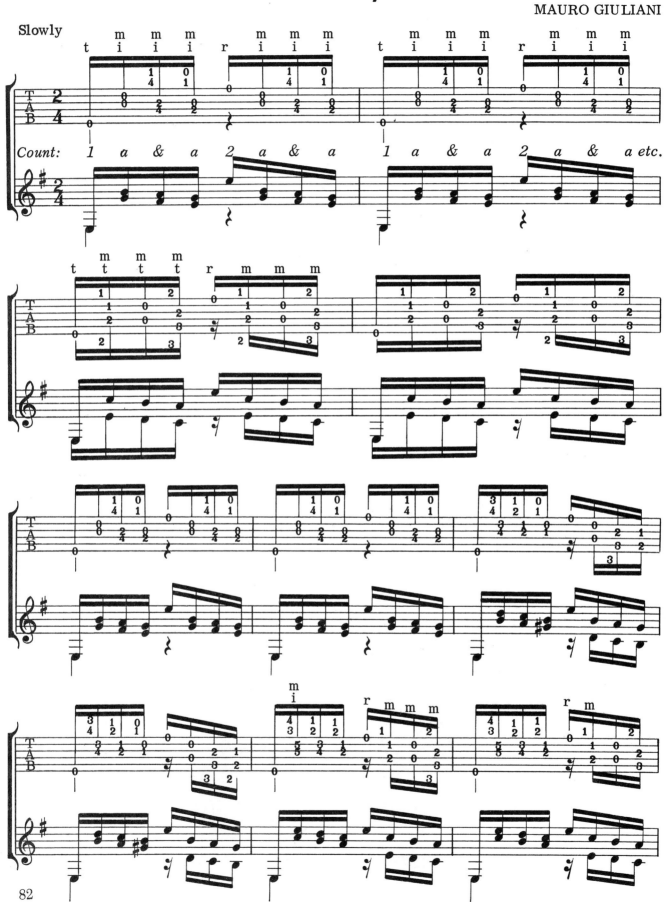

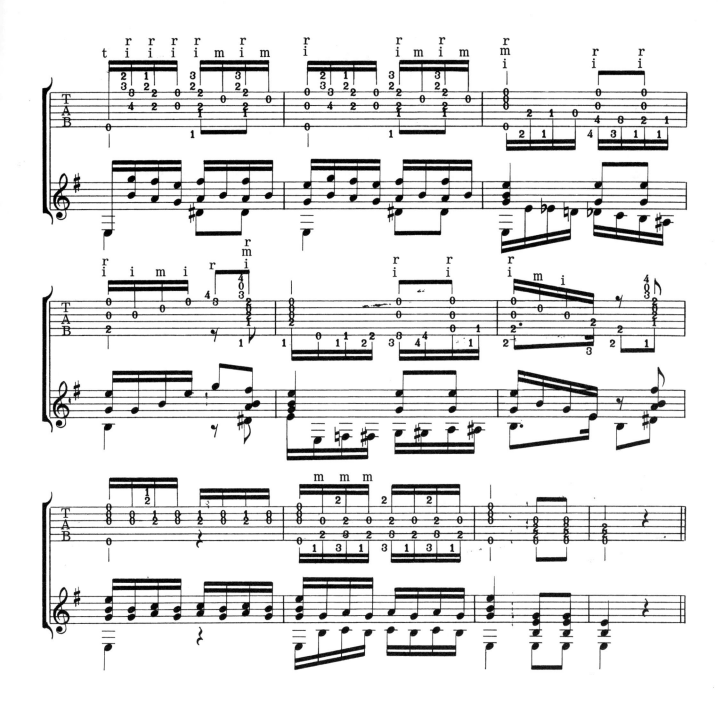

Waltz

MATTEO CACASSI

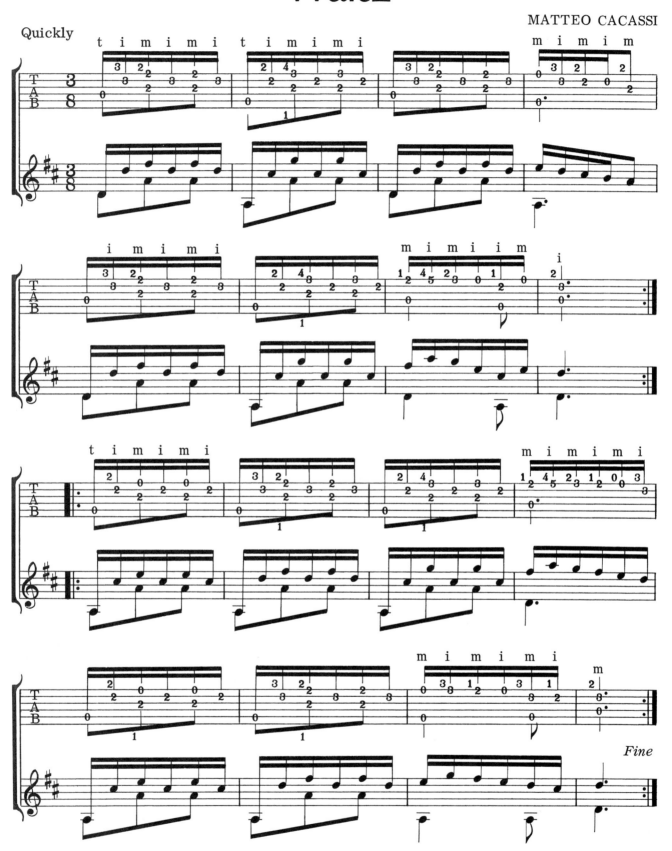

Fine

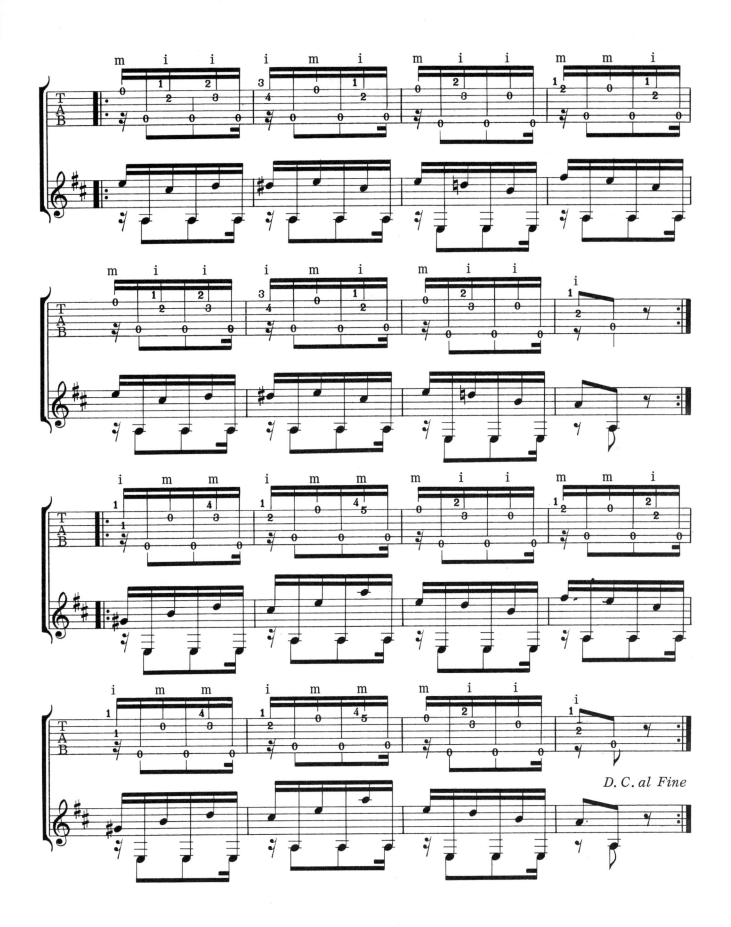

D. C. al Fine

Study

Moderately fast

MAURO GIULIANI

Study

FERNANDO CARULLI

Study

MAURO GIULIANI

Gracefully

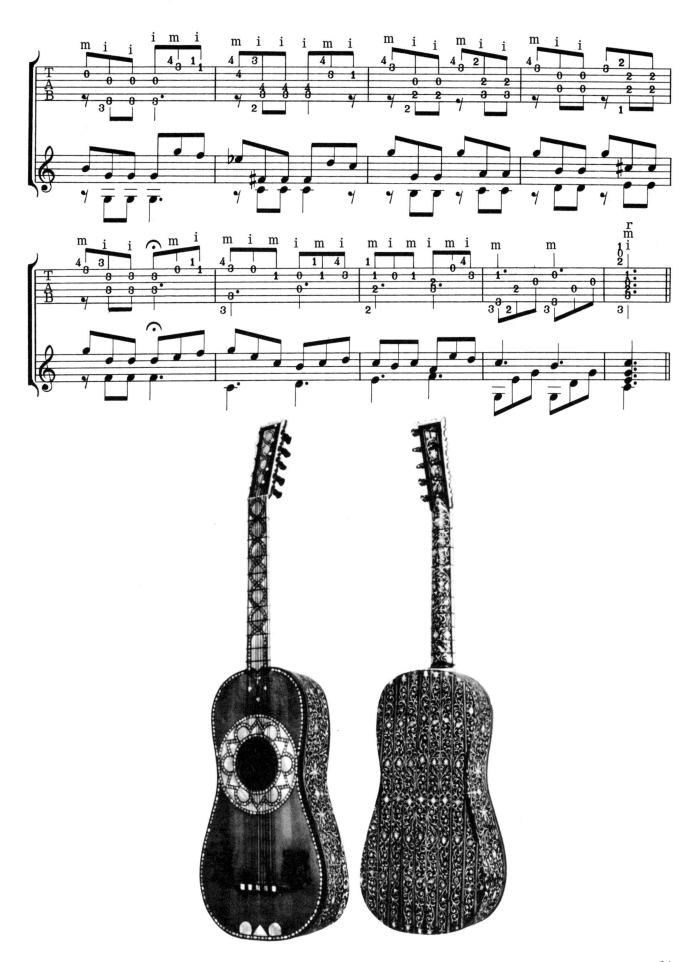

Bagatelle

ROBERT SCHUMANN
(1810–1856)

Moderately slow

Count: 3 & 4 &   1 & 2 & 3 & 4 & etc.

93

Occasionally notes are tied across the bar line. Count and play the following.

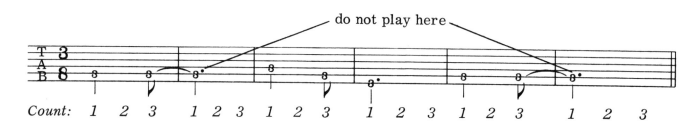

Spanish Dance

Anonymous
(17th century)

Egercicio

DIONISIO AGUADO

Moderately fast

Count: 1 & 2 & 3 & 4 & 1 & 2 & 3 & 4 & a

THE SLUR

When two notes of different pitches are tied together, the effect is called a *slur*.

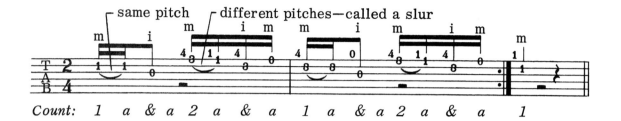

Count: *1 a & a 2 a & a 1 a & a 2 a & a 1*

The second note in any slur is made to sound by the left hand alone. This is achieved by "snapping" the left hand finger off the first note causing the second note to sound without the use of the right hand.

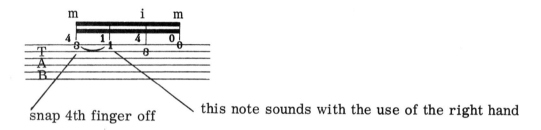

snap 4th finger off   this note sounds with the use of the right hand

Study

MAURO GIULIANI

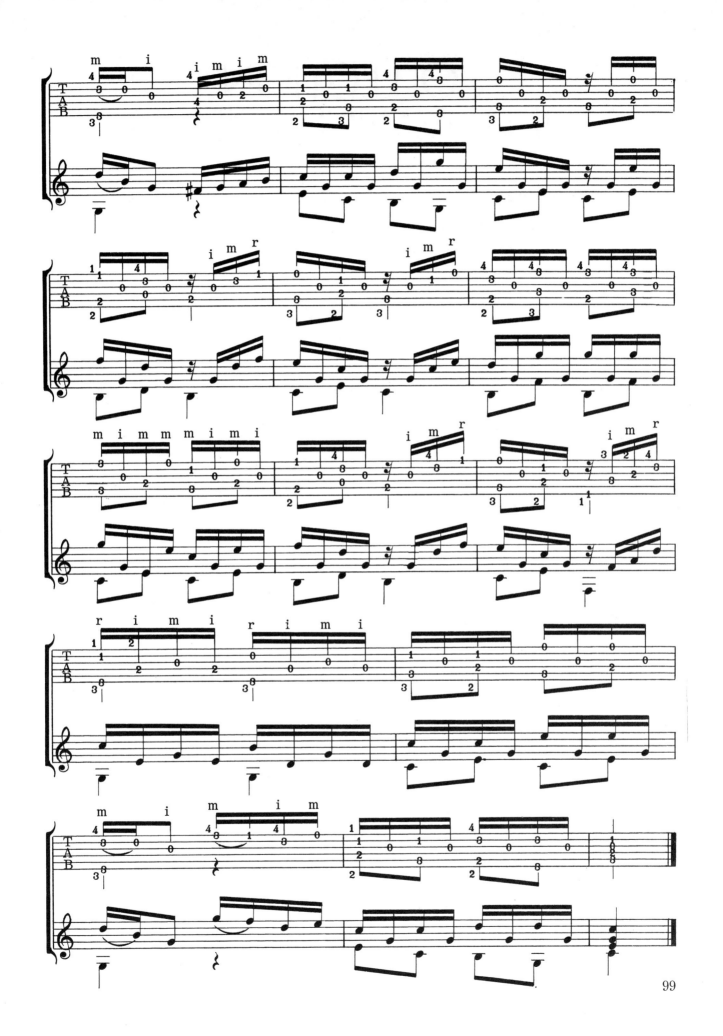

COLLECTION OF ADVANCED PIECES

The next few pieces are moderately difficult and require a competent technical ability. All but the first composition uses notes higher on the fingerboard than previously presented. As before, start learning a piece by playing it at a *slow* and *even* speed. After you can play it at slow speed without much hesitancy, gradually speed it up.

Bouree

JOHANN SEBASTIAN BACH
(1685-1750)

Study

FERNANDO SOR

Study

FERNANDO SOR

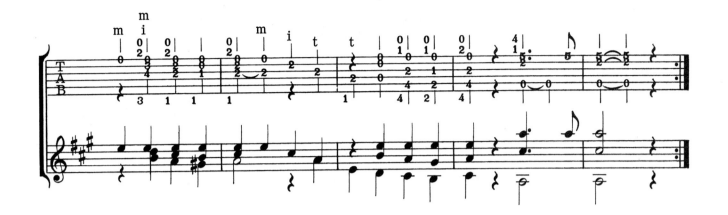

THE BAR

The last three pieces in this book make use of an advanced technique known as the *bar*. To execute a bar, simply extend the index finger of the left hand across the fingerboard fretting all six strings at one time. The fret behind which the bar is to be formed is notated in Roman numerals. (Thus B VII indicates that you form a bar behind the 7th fret.) Try this:

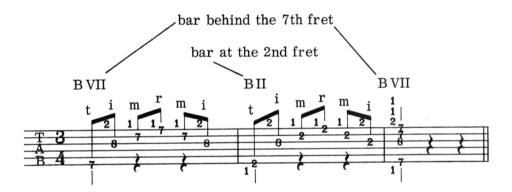

Another type of bar used in these pieces is the *half-bar* (notated ½B). A half-bar indicates that you fret two or more strings with the index finger. The next example illustrates this.

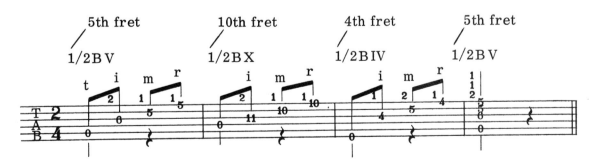

Romanza

Traditional
(19th century)

*Play the measure marked "1st ending" before you observe the re-
peat sign. When you approach this part again (after repeating) sub-
stitute the measure marked "2nd ending" for the measure marked
"1st ending" and continue.

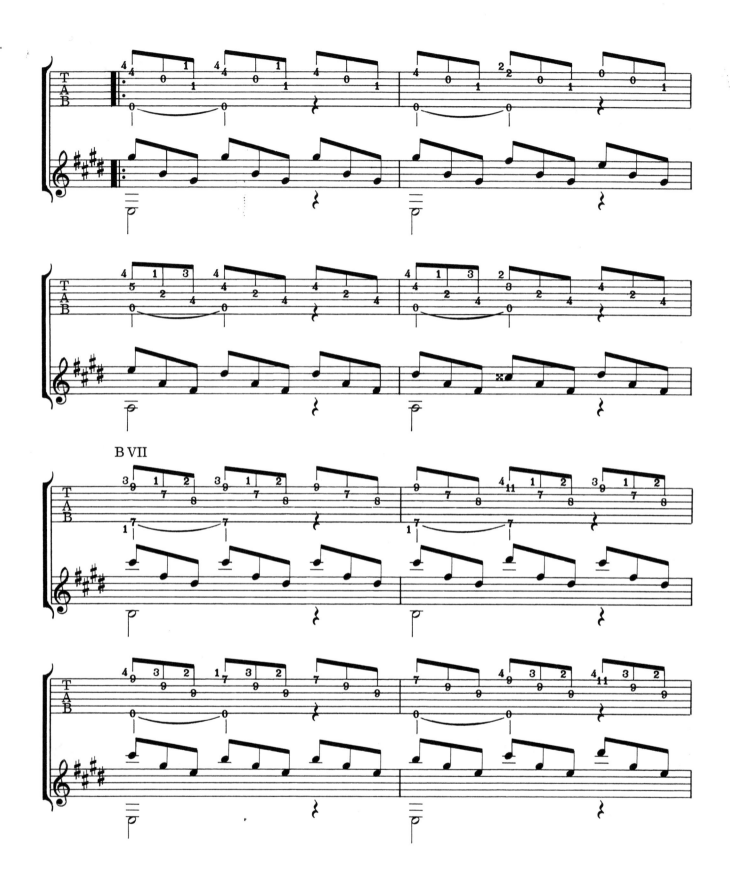

BVII

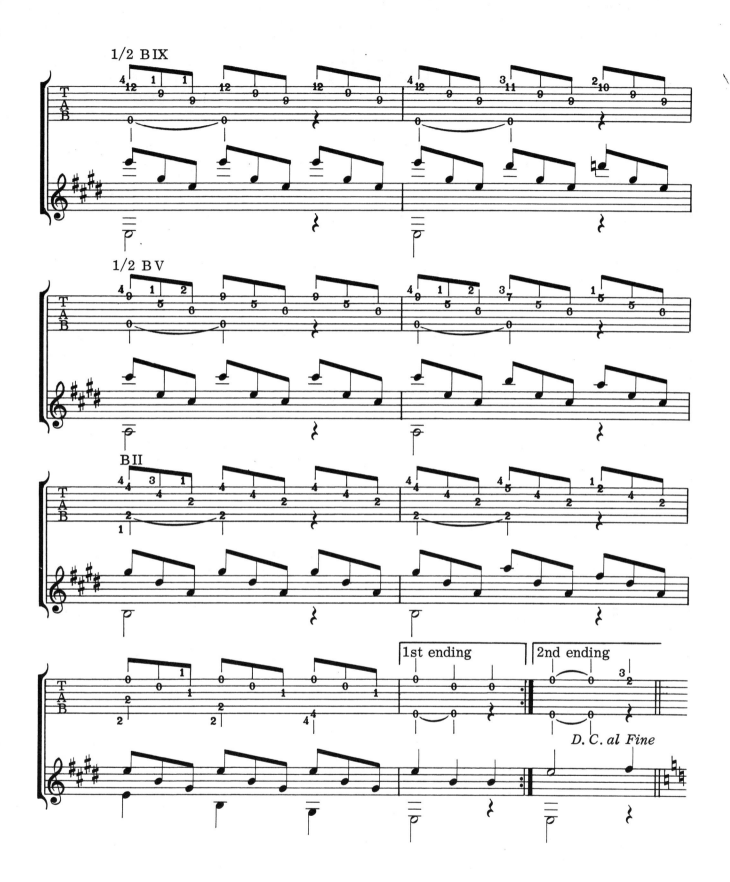

Lágrima

FRANCISCO TARREGA
(1854–1909)

*This is a slur and is played by "hammering on" the 4th finger after the note fretted by the 3rd finger is sounded.

D. C. al Fine

Study

Moderately

FERNANDO SOR